Collins

Easy Learning

Science
Age 10-11

Simon Greaves

Contents

Earth, moon and sun

What's special about the sun?

See **Q1**

The **sun** doesn't move; it's in a **fixed position**. Other things in space, like the earth, move round the sun. This is why it looks as if the sun is moving!

The sun is shaped like a **sphere**. The moon and earth are spheres too.

What's an orbit?

See **Q2**

An **orbit** is the path in which the earth, the moon or a planet travels.

The **moon** orbits the earth. It takes 28 days.

The **earth** orbits the sun. It takes 365 days.

The earth and moon are kept on their orbit by the pull of **gravity**.

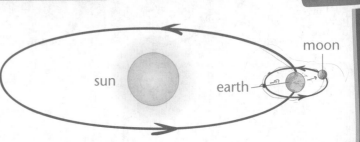

How does the earth move?

See **Q3**

As the **earth** orbits the sun, it **rotates** on its **tilted axis**.

This causes **day and night**. The part of the earth on which the sun is shining enjoys day-time, whilst on the other side of the earth it is night.

It takes 24 hours for the earth to rotate once on its axis.

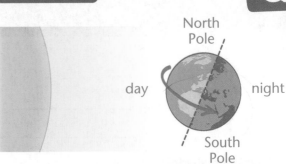

Why does the moon look different every night?

See **Q4**

The **moon** appears to be different shapes because we only see the **part** of the moon which is lit up by the sun, and this is different each day.

crescent moon   half moon   full moon   half moon   crescent moon

Q1

Does the sun move? Tick the correct answer.

a) Yes ☐ b) No ☑ c) Sometimes ☐

Q2

a) What does orbit mean? _____
_____

b) What force keeps a moon or planet in its orbit? _____

c) How long does it take the earth to orbit the sun? _____
_____

Q3

What causes day and night? Tick the correct statement.

a) The orbit of the earth. ☐

b) The rotation of the earth on its axis. ☐

c) The orbit of the moon. ☐

d) The rotation of the sun. ☐

Q4

Put the phases of the moon in the right order. Number them one to five in the boxes below.

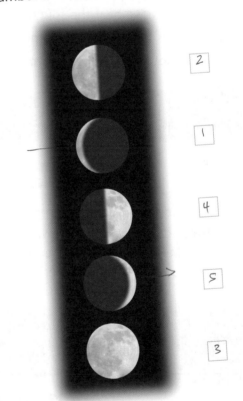

2

1

4

5

3

Quick Quiz

1 How long does it take for the earth to rotate about its axis?
_____

2 When one side of the earth is dark, what is happening on the other side?
_____

3 What shape is the earth?
_____

4 How many days does it take the moon to orbit the earth?
_____

5 What shape is the moon?
_____

Did You Know?

There are eight other planets that travel around the sun as well as the earth. They are Mercury, Venus, Mars, Jupiter, Saturn, Uranus, Neptune and Pluto.

Sound

What makes a sound?

See
Q1

All **sound** is caused by things **vibrating.**

Sounds can be made by many different things, e.g. your voice, an MP3 player and an aeroplane.

When an object stops vibrating there is no sound.

How does sound travel?

See
Q2

The vibrations of sound travel through air and other materials. When the vibrations reach our ears, we hear the sound.

Sound travels better through some materials than others, e.g. air and water.

Sound cannot travel in a **vacuum** (a space with no air in it).

What makes sound loud?

See
Q3

Some sounds are **loud** and some are **soft**.

Loudness can be varied by how hard you hit, blow, pluck or shake the object. For example, the harder you blow a recorder, the louder the sound.

What does pitch mean?

See
Q4

Pitch is a measure of how **high** or **low** a sound is.

The pitch of a sound is affected by the size and shape of the sound source.

The longer the object, the lower the pitch; e.g. a didgeridoo is very low in pitch!

a) What does an object have to do to make a sound? ....

b) Can you name two things that make sounds? ....

....

Q2

Circle the correct answers to complete this statement.

Sound can travel through:

water   metal   a vacuum   glass

Jolly Joke

Why do bagpipers walk when they play?

To get away from the sound!

Q3

Complete this musical table.

Instrument	To make a soft sound	To make a loud sound
recorder	blow gently	
drum		hit hard
guitar		

Q4

Complete these sentences.

a) The shorter the object, the .... the pitch.

b) A low sound produces a .... pitch.

Quick Quiz

1   What is the measure of how high or low a sound is?

....

2   Can sound travel through air?

....

3   What is a vacuum?

....

4   What happens when there is no noise?

....

5   What is the measure of how loud or soft a sound is?

....

Did You Know?

Sound is measured in **decibels**.

Whispering	10 decibels
Noisy classroom	70 decibels
Lawnmower	90 decibels
Jet fighter	130 decibels

Light and shadow

See Q1

How does light travel?

Light travels in **straight lines** from a light source (e.g. the sun, light bulb, lighted candle) and bounces off objects. We can see the objects because the light from them travels to our eyes.

See Q2

Can light travel through some objects?

Light travels completely through **transparent** materials, such as glass. Light cannot travel through **opaque** materials, such as brick and cardboard. **Translucent** materials, such as tissue paper, allow some light to pass through them.

See Q3

Do some materials reflect light?

Light is reflected by **shiny** objects. Mirrors and metal reflect light well, whilst dull, dark objects do not.

See Q4

How is a shadow formed?

A **shadow** is formed when an object **blocks out** light. The closer an object is to the light source, the larger the shadow.

torch close to glove puppet   torch far away from glove puppet

See Q5

How does the sun affect the length of shadows during the day?

During the day the sun appears to move across the sky, although it is actually the earth that moves. The sun is our main light source and the **shadows** it casts are **shortest** at midday and **longest** at the beginning and the end of the day.

Q1

Which of the following is **not** a source of light? Ring your answer.

mirror   torch

sun   switched-on TV

Q2

Draw lines to join each material to the word that best describes it.

tissue paper   opaque

clear glass bottle   translucent

piece of cardboard   transparent

Q3

Circle the objects which reflect light well.

CD   mirror   carpet

foil   blackboard

Q4

What is formed when an object blocks out light?

Shadow

Q5

The shadows cast at midday are the longest during the day. True or false?

FALSE

Quick Quiz

1 How does light travel?

2 What sort of object reflects light best?

3 What is meant by opaque?

4 What word is used to describe a material that lets some light pass through it?

5 What is our main light source?

Did You Know?

It takes $8\frac{1}{2}$ minutes for light to travel from the sun to the earth.

Electricity

See Q1

Where do we get electricity from?

We get **electricity** from the **mains** or from **batteries**.
Cookers, hairdryers and TVs use electricity from the mains.
Mobile phones, clocks and torches use electricity from batteries.

See Q2

What is needed to make an electrical circuit?

An **electrical circuit** needs a **power source**
(e.g. a battery), **wires** and other devices such
as **motors**, **buzzers** and **bulbs**. If the wires
are connected correctly to the battery, electricity
will flow.

Adding an extra battery or shortening the wires
will make the bulb shine more brightly.

yes

no

See Q3

What is a switch used for?

A **switch** is used to **break** the flow of electricity in a circuit, e.g. to switch a bulb on and off.

See Q4

What is a circuit diagram?

A **circuit diagram** uses **symbols** to
show the parts of a circuit. This diagram
shows a circuit containing a battery, bulb
and closed switch.

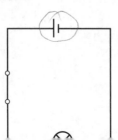

Here are the symbols you need to know.

battery

bulb

motor

buzzer

switch (off)

switch (on)

Q1

Write mains or battery next to each type of electrical appliance.

dishwasher ....

torch.................................

cooker ....

mobile phone ....

Q2

Tick which of the circuits would work.

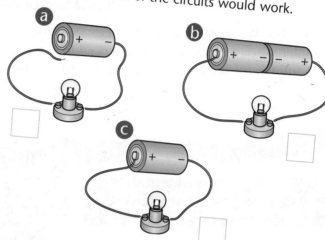

Q3

What is a switch used for?

....

....

Q4

Tick which of the circuit diagrams shows the circuit in the picture.

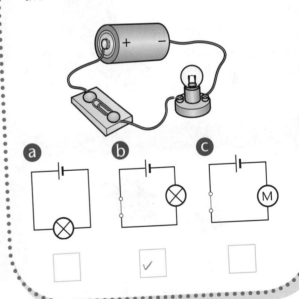

Quick Quiz

1 What effect will shortening the wires have on the brightness of a bulb in a circuit?

....

2 Draw the symbol for a motor.

(M)

....

3 What device is used to break the flow of electricity in a circuit?

Switch

....

4 Name a power source that can be used in a circuit.

Battay

....

5 Give a reason why a torch might not work.

....

Did You Know?

The first battery was made in 1800 by Alessandro Volta. The electrical units of volts are named after him.

Forces

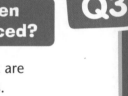

See Q1

What is a force?

A **force** is a **push** or a **pull**. Forces can be different sizes and act in different directions. **Arrows** are used in diagrams to show forces. A force is measured in **newtons** (N) using a forcemeter.

1 N

See Q2

What happens when forces are balanced?

When forces acting on an object are **balanced**, the object stays **still**.

The force from each hand is the same size so the hands push together and don't move.

The arrows showing the forces are the same size but point in opposite directions.

See Q3

What happens when forces are unbalanced?

When forces acting on an object are **unbalanced**, the object **moves**.

The force from the left hand is larger, so the left hand pushes the right hand over.

The arrows showing the forces are different sizes and point in opposite directions.

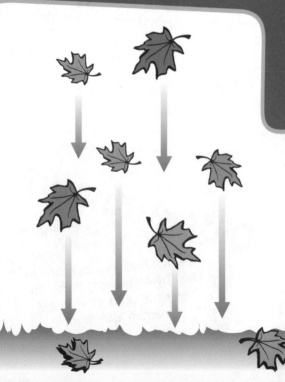

See Q4

What is the effect of gravity on objects?

Gravity is the **downward pull** of the earth towards its centre. All objects on the earth feel this force. The force caused by gravity on an object is called **weight**.

Q1

a) What is a force? ....

b) In which units are forces measured?

....

Q2

Beth and Bill are pulling on each end of a rope. They are both pulling with a force so that neither of them moves. Tick the picture in which the arrows correctly show the forces acting.

Q3

Here are three toy cars. There are two forces acting on each car. Tick which of the three cars will move forwards.

Q4

What is the force on an object that is caused by gravity? Circle the correct word.

newtons   mass

weight   heavy

Quick Quiz

1 Which piece of equipment is used to measure force?

....

2 How do you show forces on a diagram?

....

3 For an object to move, the forces acting on it must be

....

4 For an object to stay still, the forces acting on it must be

....

5 If you drop a pencil why does it always fall to the floor?

....

Did You Know?

Gravity exists on the moon as well as on the earth, but the effect is not as strong.

Types of forces

See Q1

Why does an object float in water?

Upthrust is the upward push of an object in water. If the upthrust is the **same** size as the weight of the object it will **float**.

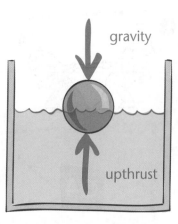

gravity

upthrust

See Q2

What is friction?

Friction is a force that tries to stop objects sliding against each other. Friction can be reduced by making the surfaces of the objects smoother. Sometimes we need friction, e.g. to give grip between the tyres on a car and the road.

force driving car

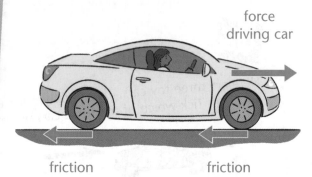

friction   friction

See Q3

What is the effect of air resistance?

There is some friction between the air and things moving in it. This is called **air resistance**. Air resistance slows down objects moving through it.

air resistance

gravity

See Q4

What type of force acts between magnets?

Magnets exert **magnetic forces** on each other. Magnets have two **poles**: north and south. When **opposite** poles are placed together the magnets **attract** each other (stick together). When the **same** poles are placed together they **repel** each other (push apart).

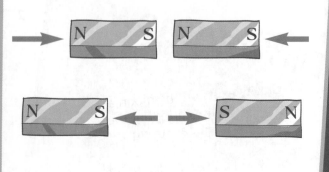

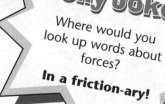

Q1

Complete this sentence.

If the upthrust of a ball in water is the same size as the weight of the ball it will ....

Q2

Put a tick in the correct column for each situation.

Situation	Want friction	Don't want friction
car tyres on a road		
ice skates on an ice rink		
trainers on a tennis court		

Q3

Draw an arrow on the diagram to show the force of air resistance acting on the feather as it falls through the air. Think carefully about the size and direction of the arrow.

gravity

Q4

Write next to each pair of magnets whether they will attract or repel each other.

....

....

....

Quick Quiz

1 Is the force of friction greater between rough or smooth surfaces?

....

2 What are opposite ends of a magnet called?

....

3 What is the force that acts on an object moving through the air?

....

4 For an object in water, what happens if the upthrust is less than the object's weight?

....

5 What happens when opposite poles of magnets are placed together?

....

Did You Know?

About 2200 years ago, the Greek mathematician Archimedes is said to have discovered upthrust whilst having a bath.

Living things

What is a living thing?

See Q1

Plants and **animals** are living things. All living things are able to grow, feed, reproduce, get rid of waste, breathe, respond to changes and move.

What is growth?

See Q2

Growth is the process by which a young living thing grows into an adult.

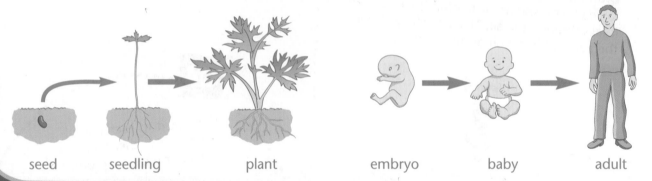

seed seedling   plant   embryo   baby   adult

What is nutrition?

See Q3

Nutrition is the way in which a living thing **feeds**. Plants make their own food in their leaves. Animals and humans eat other plants and animals.

What is reproduction?

See Q4

Reproduction is how new living things are created. Green plants produce **seeds** which grow into young plants. In animals, including humans, **fertilised eggs** develop into young animals.

What is movement?

See Q5

Animals and humans are able to **move** around and move different parts of their body on their own. Plants cannot move from one place to another but they do turn to face a source of light (e.g. the sun).

Q1

Unscramble the words to reveal three things that all living things can do.

etahber   rrcdoupee   wrog

breathe   ....

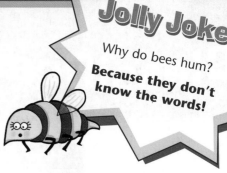

Q2

Put these words in the correct order to show the stages of growth.

a) seedling   plant   seed

....

b) adult   baby   embryo

....

Q3

What is the process by which living things feed?

....

Q4

Complete this sentence by filling in the blanks.

.... is the process by which

new plants are created. Green plants produce

.... which grow into young plants.

Q5

Write whether each statement is true or false.

a) Animals can move to different

places. ....

b) Humans can move parts of

their bodies. ....

c) Plants can move to other

places. ....

Quick Quiz

1 Name two things that all living things can do.

....

....

2 By what process does a young animal change into an adult animal?

....

3 Where do plants make their food?

....

4 What do green plants grow from?

....

5 In what way can plants move?

....

Did You Know?

An elephant's pregnancy lasts 22 months compared to 9 months for a human. It is the longest of any mammal.

Classification and keys

See **Q1**

How do we classify living things?

Plants and animals can be grouped together (**classified**) by the things (**characteristics**) they have in common, e.g. backbone, wings or flowers. Each group has a special name.

See **Q2**

How are plants classified?

There are two main groups of plants: those that flower and those that do not.

See **Q3**

How are animals classified?

There are two main groups of animals: those with a backbone (**vertebrates**) and those without (**invertebrates**).

- **Vertebrates** include mammals (e.g. cats, humans), birds, fish, reptiles (e.g. snakes, crocodiles), amphibians (e.g. frogs, newts)

- **Invertebrates** include animals such as beetles, slugs, spiders, earwigs

See **Q4**

What is a key?

A **key** is a diagram that is used to **identify** an unknown living thing by studying its characteristics. Here is an example of a key.

This animal can be identified by using this key.

Has it got four legs?

yes — no

Does it have a tail?

Does it have feathers?

no — yes — no — yes

hamster — shrew — trout — wren

Q1

How are animals and plants put into groups?

....

....

Q2

What are the two main groups of plants? Underline the correct answer.

a) Trees and flowers

b) Flowering plants and non-flowering plants

c) Fruit and vegetables

Q3

Put these animals into the correct column in the table.

parrot   worm   frog   slug

woodlouse   dog

Vertebrates	Invertebrates

Q4

Use the key to identify this animal.

A

Has it got six legs

yes → no →

Has it got wings?   Has it got feathers?

yes ↓   no ↓   no ↓   yes ↓

bluebottle   ant   salamander   sparrow

A is ....

Quick Quiz

1 What is a vertebrate?

....

2 Give an example of an invertebrate.

....

3 What is a key used for?

....

4 A rose is a flowering plant. True or false?

....

5 To which group of animals do frogs and newts belong?

....

Did You Know?

The largest living vertebrate is the blue whale. It can grow to about 25 metres long.

Habitats and adaptation

See Q1

What is a habitat?

A **habitat** is a place where a plant or animal lives. Habitats can be large or small, e.g. a desert or a garden pond. Animals and plants are suited (**adapted**) to live in their habitats.

See Q2

How are animals and plants adapted to their habitats?

This garden shows the habitats of some animals and plants and how they are adapted to them.

thrush – camouflaged by bushes and trees, eats worms and berries, so lives in the garden

fern – doesn't need much light so lives in shade

earthworm – has bristles and can burrow as it lives on and in the soil

frog – lays eggs in water and feeds on insects so lives in or near the pond

See Q3

Which features make animals suited to their way of life?

A heron has a sharp beak to catch fish. A polar bear has thick fur to keep it warm in a very cold climate. A fish has gills so that it can breathe under water.

Q1

What is a habitat?

....

....

Q2

Draw lines to join the animal to its correct habitat.

  frog   soil

  earthworm   shade

  fern   hedges and trees

  thrush   pond

Q3

Tick the features of a fish that make it suited to a life in water.

a) It breathes through gills. ☐

b) It breathes through lungs. ☐

c) It has webbed feet. ☐

d) It has a long tongue. ☐

e) It has fins. ☐

Did You Know?

In deserts the only water many animals get is that which is in moist plants and the blood of their prey.

Quick Quiz

1 What sort of habitat has hot and dry conditions?

....

2 Where does a frog lay its eggs?

....

3 Why does a heron have a sharp beak?

....

4 Name one feature of a kestrel that helps it to catch its prey.

....

5 Name an animal that lives in a very cold climate.

....

Food chains

See Q1

Who eats what?

Everything we and other living things eat is **linked**. These links between plants and animals are called **food chains**. Most food chains start with a **green plant**.

Lettuce ⟶ snail ⟶ thrush ⟶ cat

See Q2

What are producers and consumers?

All **plants** are **producers** because they **make** their own food. All **animals** are **consumers** because they **eat** other plants and animals. For example, a thrush eats snails, worms and insects as well as berries and fruits.

What is a predator?

See Q3

A **predator** is an animal that gets its food by eating other animals. The animal that a predator eats is called its **prey**. For example, a fox will kill and eat a rabbit.

See Q4

Can an animal or plant be in two different food chains?

Some animals and plants can be part of more than one food chain. For example:

rose ⟶ **greenfly** ⟶ ladybird

lupin ⟶ **greenfly** ⟶ frog ⟶ heron

Q1

Complete the food chain using these three living things.

slug   hedgehog   lettuce

[   ] → [   ] → [   ]

Q2

Write each living thing in the correct column of the table.

rabbit   slug   lettuce

grass   greenfly

Producers	Consumers

Q3

a) What is a predator?

....

....

b) What is prey?

....

....

Q4

Here are two food chains. Choose the living thing from the list below that appears in both food chains.

fly   rabbit   deer   cabbage

[grass] → [   ] → [fox]

[lettuce] → [   ] → [stoat]

Quick Quiz

1 What do most food chains start with?

....

2 What are all plants in a food chain classed as?

....

3 What are all animals in a food chain classed as?

....

4 Is a fox a predator?

....

5 A plant can be part of more than one food chain. True or false?

....

21

Plant growth

See Q1

What are the main parts of a plant?

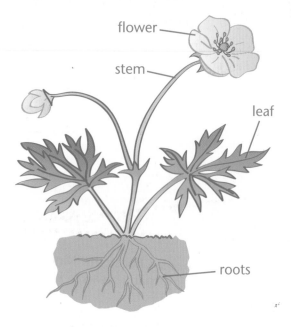

flower

stem

leaf

roots

flower – used in reproduction

stem – carries water and nutrients

leaves – make food and get rid of oxygen

roots – take up water and nutrients, anchor the plant

See Q2

How does a plant grow?

A seed **germinates** (starts to grow) and produces a young plant. The young plant grows into an adult plant with flowers. The flowers produce **pollen** which is used in **reproduction** to produce new **seeds**.

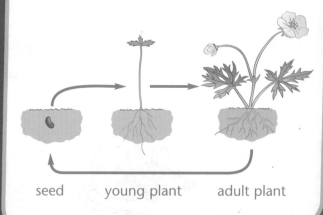

seed   young plant   adult plant

See Q3

What does a plant need to grow well?

A plant needs air, light, heat, water and nutrients (food). A plant takes carbon dioxide from the air, and with water and light, creates sugar for food and makes oxygen.

See Q4

What happens if a plant is neglected?

If a plant is not watered, its leaves will fall off and the stem will shrivel. If a plant does not get enough light, its leaves will turn yellow and become spindly. If a plant is too cold, it will stop growing.

Q1

Draw lines to join each part of the plant to its purpose.

stem   makes food

leaf   used in reproduction

roots   carries water

flower   anchor the plant

Now label these four parts of the plant on the diagram.

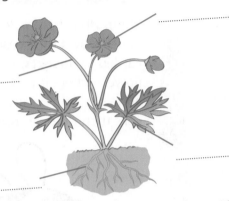

....

....

....

....

Jolly Joke

What kind of tree do fingers grow on?

A palm tree!

Q2

Complete the life cycle of a plant using the words given.

young plant   seed   plant dies   adult plant

seed dispersal →

germination

growth

pollination

Q3

Unscramble the words to spell out four things that a plant needs for healthy growth.

tninreust ....

tglih ....

teha ....

trawe ....

Q4

Tick the correct answer to complete the sentence.

Yellow leaves on a plant are a sign of...

a) lack of light. ☐

b) lack of water. ☐

c) lack of heat. ☐

Quick Quiz

1 Through which part of a plant is water taken in?

....

2 What would a plant that hasn't been watered look like?

....

3 What is the main purpose of the leaves on a plant?

....

4 What is the name of the process by which a seed starts to grow?

....

5 Name two things a plant needs for healthy growth.

....

Did You Know?

The tallest sunflower ever grown was almost 8 metres tall.

Flowering plants

See Q1

What are the main parts of a flower?

The **flower** is used in plant **reproduction**.

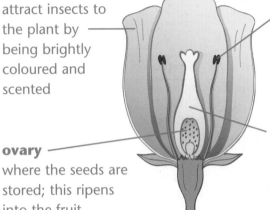

petals
attract insects to the plant by being brightly coloured and scented

stamen
the male part of the plant which produces pollen

ovary
where the seeds are stored; this ripens into the fruit

carpel
the female part of the plant, made up of the stigma, style and ovary

See Q2

Why does a flower have pollen?

The **pollen** from a flower is either blown by the **wind**, or carried by **insects**, to other flowers where it **fertilises** the egg cells in the ovary. These cells then produce **seeds**.

See Q3

What happens to the seeds?

The seeds from a flower are **dispersed** (scattered around). Some seeds are blown long distances by the **wind**. Other seeds are eaten by **animals** and passed out in their waste. In some plants, seeds **explode** from their pods; some of the seeds fall in soil and **germinate** (start to grow).

seed

dandelion

seed

strawberry

seed

sweet pea

24

Q1

Draw lines to join each part of the flower to its purpose.

stamen   where seeds are stored

ovary   attracts insects

petal   male part of the flower

Now label these three parts of the flower on the diagram.

....

....

....

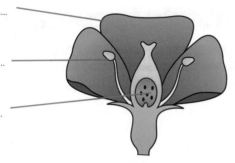

Q2

Give two ways in which pollen is carried to other flowers.

1 ....

2 ....

Q3

Seeds are dispersed in different ways. Which of these is the odd one out?

a) Blown by the wind ☐

b) Eaten by a bird ☐

c) Carried by a bee ☐

Quick Quiz

1 Which three things make up the female part of a flower?

....

2 Why does pollen stick to the legs of insects?

....

3 How are the seeds of a dandelion dispersed?

....

4 What do fertilised eggs produce in a flower?

....

5 How do you think raspberry seeds are scattered?

....

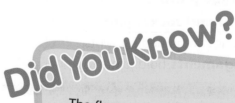

Did You Know?

The flower of the Titan Arum plant can grow up to 3.5 metres high and it smells of rotting flesh.

Human body

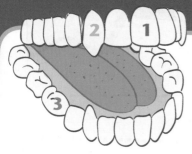

What are the 3 types of teeth?

1 inciscors to **cut**   **2** canines to **tear**   **3** molars to **chew**

See Q1

Omnivores (e.g. humans) have all three types of teeth. They eat plants and animals.
Herbivores (plant eaters) have **incisors** to cut plants, and **molars** to grind plants.
Carnivores (meat eaters) have **canines** to grip and tear flesh, and **molars** to crush bones.

See Q2

How can I have healthy teeth?

Sugar in food attracts **bacteria** in the mouth, which produces **plaque** on the teeth.
Plaque produces acid which causes **decay**.

To avoid tooth decay ✓ brush twice a day ✓ use dental floss ✓ visit your dentist
✓ eat healthy foods ✓ drink milk which contains calcium

What are the skeleton's 3 jobs?

1 **Protects** vital organs e.g. skull protects brain,
   ribs protect heart and lungs
2 **Supports** your body
3 Enables **movement**

See Q3

What are the 2 main types of joints?

1 **Hinge joints** e.g. knee and elbow
2 **Ball and socket joints** e.g. hip and shoulder
   Bones are joined by joints.
   Ligaments hold joints together.

How do muscles work?

Muscles are attached to
bones. They move the bones
by **contracting** and **relaxing**.
Muscles work in **pairs** e.g. the
triceps and biceps in your arm.
Muscles can only **pull**, they
cannot push.

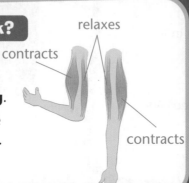

relaxes
contracts
contracts

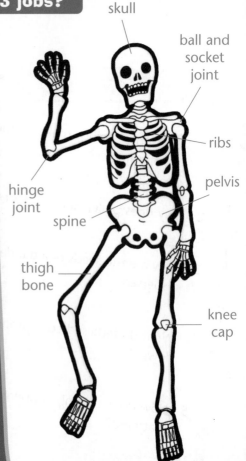

skull
ball and
socket
joint
ribs
pelvis
hinge
joint
spine
thigh
bone
knee
cap

Q1

Circle the odd one out each time.

a) incisor   molar   plaque   canine

b) carnivore   canine   omnivore   herbivore

Q2

Complete this poem using these words.

| tooth | floss | plaque | twice |

.... can cause teeth to decay,

So brush your teeth .... a day.

Try to use some dental .... ,

This will help to stop .... loss.

Q3

Help the skeleton through the maze to find his skeleton friend. Your route must only go through true skeleton and joints facts.

a skeleton is jointed

the skeleton is made of chalk

ligaments hold joints together

the skeleton enables movement

ribs protect heart and lungs

start

the skull protects the stomach

the shoulder is a hinge joint

the knee is a ball and socket joint

finish

Quick Quiz

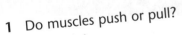

1 Do muscles push or pull?

....

2 Which type of tooth is used to chew food?

....

3 Do muscles work in pairs?

....

4 Which mineral is good for healthy teeth and bones?

....

5 What do carnivores mostly eat?

....

Did You Know?

There are 206 bones in the human skeleton.

The smallest bone is the stirrup, which is found in the middle ear.

Health and healthy eating

What is a healthy diet?

A **healthy diet** contains foods of different types in the right amounts. A healthy diet also includes plenty of **water**.

See Q1

Food type	Needed for	Found in
carbohydrates	energy	cereals, pasta, sugar
protein	growth and repair	fish, meat, eggs
fats	stored energy	butter, cheese
vitamins and minerals	healthy body	fruit, vegetables
fibre	digestion	cereals, fruit, vegetables

See Q2

Why is the heart an important organ?

The **heart** is a powerful **muscle** which pumps blood around the body. When we breathe, **oxygen** is taken into the blood and **carbon dioxide** is removed from it.

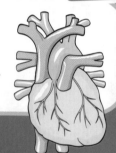

See Q3

Why is regular exercise good for your heart?

When you **exercise** your heart has to work harder to get oxygen to the working muscles. This makes your heart stronger.

Your **pulse** is a measure of **heart rate** in beats per minute. The quicker your pulse, the harder your heart is working.

See Q4

Which things are bad for your health?

Smoking cigarettes, drinking too much alcohol, lack of exercise and a poor diet are all damaging to your health.

Q1

Draw lines to join each food to its correct food group.

carbohydrates

protein

fats

vitamins and minerals

Q2

Use the following words to complete the sentences.

| oxygen | carbon dioxide |
| heart | blood |

.... is pumped around the

body by the ....

The blood carries .... to the

body and removes ....

.... from it.

Q3

a) What is your pulse a measure of?

....

b) Why is exercise good for the heart?

....

....

Q4

Circle the things below that are bad for your health.

regular exercise

too much alcohol

balanced diet

smoking

Quick Quiz

1 Which two types of food provide energy?

....

2 What is fibre in food good for?

....

3 Which muscle pumps blood?

....

4 How would you expect your pulse rate to change during exercise?

....

5 Which gas is taken into the blood when we breathe?

....

Did You Know?

A child's body is made up of about 75% (three-quarters) water.

Micro-organisms

What are micro-organisms?

Micro-organisms are **very small** living things which can only be seen through a powerful **microscope**. Micro-organisms are found in food, water and air, as well as on and inside humans and animals.

See Q1

Why are some micro-organisms harmful to us?

See Q2

Many **illnesses** and **infections** are caused by micro-organisms. The common cold is caused by a type of micro-organism called a **virus**. Plaque which causes tooth decay contains **bacteria**. **Mould** is a type of micro-organism found on decaying food.

How can we stop spreading harmful micro-organisms?

See Q3

- Wash your hands before eating and after going to the toilet.
- Cover your nose and mouth when you sneeze.
- Keep away from other people who have an infection.
- Don't eat food which is not fresh or properly cooked.

Are some micro-organisms helpful?

See Q4

Some micro-organisms are helpful, e.g. **yeast** is used to make bread. **Yoghurt** also contains a healthy bacteria.

Q1

Ring the piece of equipment you would need to use to see a micro-organism.

magnifying glass   camera

microscope   telescope

Q2

Unscramble these words which are types of harmful micro-organisms.

lomud   iatbrcea   sivru

....

Q3

List three ways in which you can prevent the spread of harmful micro-organisms.

1 ....

2 ....

3 ....

Q4

Which helpful micro-organism is used in making bread?

....

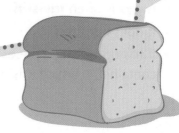

Quick Quiz

1 What is a micro-organism?

....

2 Name two places in which micro-organisms can be found.

....

3 What does plaque contain that causes tooth decay?

....

4 Which type of micro-organism is the common cold an example of?

....

5 Why should you wash your hands after going to the toilet?

....

Did You Know?

Alexander Fleming discovered penicillin which is used to cure infections caused by harmful bacteria.

States of matter

What is a solid?

See Q1

- A **solid** can be **held** and has a **definite** shape.
- It can be cut or shaped.

Be careful! Some solids like sand, sugar and flour can be poured but each **particle** has a definite shape.

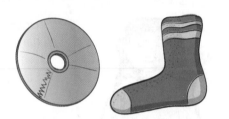

What is a liquid?

See Q2

- A **liquid flows** downwards.
- It takes up the shape of the container in which it is held.
- A liquid can be **poured** and is not easy to hold.

What is a gas?

See Q3

- A **gas** is often **invisible**.
- It does not flow.
- It fills up **empty spaces** or the container in which it is held.

steam

helium-filled balloon

Can states of matter be changed?

See Q4

When some solids are **heated** they can change into a liquid or a gas. Some gases when **cooled** change into liquids or solids.

For example, water is a liquid at room temperature. If it is cooled in a freezer it turns into ice (a solid). If water is heated to a high enough temperature it turns

ice: **solid**

water: **liquid**

Q1

Complete the sentences by filling in the blanks.

a) A solid has a .... shape.

b) A solid can .... in your hands.

Q2

Circle the liquids in the list below.

water   sand   syrup

paper   milk   chocolate

Q3

Tick the correct properties of a gas.

a) It does not flow. ☐

b) It can be cut. ☐

c) It flows downwards. ☐

d) It is usually invisible. ☐

Q4

Complete the boxes in each picture using either solid, liquid or gas.

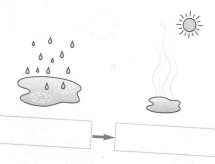

☐ → ☐

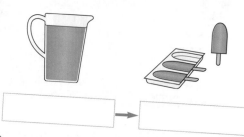

☐ → ☐

Quick Quiz

Look at the bottle of cola and write either solid, liquid or gas for each part of the object.

cap: ☐

air: ☐

bottle: ☐

cola: ☐

bubbles: ☐

Did You Know?

Mercury is the only metal which is a liquid at room temperature. All other metals are solids.

Reversible and non-reversible changes

See Q1

What is a reversible change?

A **reversible** change is when you can **get back** the material you started with. For example, water which has been frozen into ice will melt at room temperature back to water. A **physical** change has taken place.

water freezes ⟶ ice ⟶ ice melts ⟶ water

See Q2

What is the water cycle?

The **water cycle** is an example of a **reversible** change.

See Q3

What is a non-reversible change?

A **non-reversible** change is when the material is **permanently** changed. It cannot be reversed. For example, when a piece of bread is heated under a grill it changes to toast. The toast cannot be changed back into bread. A **chemical** change has taken place.

a Water evaporates (changes from liquid to gas) from seas and rivers

b Clouds are formed by water vapour condensing (changing from gas to liquid)

c Clouds cool to form water droplets

d Water droplets fall as rain into seas and rivers

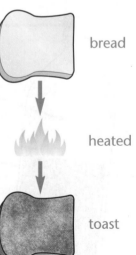

bread

heated

toast

Q1

Complete these sentences.

a) A .... change is one in which you can get back the material you started with.

b) Water .... to make ice. Ice .... to give water.

Q2

Put the four stages of the water cycle in the correct order.

a) Clouds cool to form water droplets

b) Clouds are formed by water vapour condensing

c) Water droplets fall as rain into seas and rivers

d) Water evaporates from seas and rivers

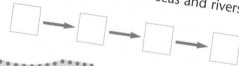

Q3

If an egg is warmed it starts to change: the clear part of the egg starts to turn white as it begins to cook.

a) Is this change reversible or non-reversible? ....

b) Give a reason for your answer.

....

....

Did You Know?

When rain in clouds freezes it makes tiny ice crystals. As these crystals fall from the clouds, they start to melt and stick together to form big snowflakes.

Quick Quiz

1 Ice lollies may be melted into fruit juice. What type of change is this?

....

2 The water cycle is an example of a non-reversible change. True or false?

....

3 Chocolate may be melted into a liquid. What sort of change is this?

....

4 Is a reversible change a physical or chemical change?

....

5 When water evaporates it changes from a liquid to a what?

....

Mixing materials

See Q1

What is a mixture?

A **mixture** is made up of two or more **materials**. Some are made up of solids, e.g. sand and pebbles. Some are made by dissolving a solid in a liquid. This is called a **solution**.

See Q2

See Q3

How can a mixture of solids be separated?

Sieving separates some mixtures of solids e.g. rice grains and flour. The smaller flour particles pass through the sieve whilst the larger rice grains don't.

How can a mixture of a solid in a liquid be separated?

Filtering can be used to separate some mixtures of solids in liquids, e.g. sand in water. The particles of sand cannot pass through the filter paper but the water can.

See Q4

See Q5

Are there any other ways of separating solids from liquids?

Evaporation separates some mixtures of a solid in a liquid. A solution of salt in water is separated by boiling the solution until the water has evaporated. The salt will be left as a solid in the dish.

What mixtures can't be separated?

When **plaster of Paris** is mixed with water, it forms a thick liquid which then sets into a solid. This mixture cannot be separated. It is **non-reversible**. A mixture of **vinegar and bicarbonate of soda** can't be separated either.

Jolly Joke

What did the dentist say when his wife was mixing together a cake?

Can I do the filling?!

Q1

What do you get if you dissolve a solid in a liquid?

....

Q2

Here are three mixtures of two solids. Each mixture is poured into a kitchen sieve. Write down which, if any, materials will pass through the sieve for each mixture.

sugar and flour

rice and sand

rice and dried peas

....

Q3

Choose the correct word from the list to complete the sentence.

| sieving | filtering | dissolving |

Sand can be separated from water by
.... the mixture.

Q4

How could you remove the salt from sea water?

....
....

Q5

Tick the mixture that cannot be separated.

a) Sugar and water ☐

b) Sand and rice ☐

c) Vinegar and bicarbonate of soda ☐

Quick Quiz

1   What is a mixture made up of?

....

2   Which piece of equipment could be used to separate rice and flour?

....

3   Salt can be separated from water by filtering. True or false?

....

4   Can all mixtures be separated in some way?

....

5   When salt is removed from water by boiling, where does the water go?

....

Did You Know?

Air is a mixture of gases including nitrogen, oxygen, argon, hydrogen, carbon dioxide, water vapour, helium and others.

Properties of materials

See Q1

What is a natural material?

A **natural material** is one that occurs in nature, e.g. oil, diamond, iron and silk. Some materials are not natural but are **man-made**, e.g. nylon, PVC and fibre glass.

See Q2

What sort of properties do materials have?

Different materials have different properties so are used for different purposes.

Property	Materials	Uses	Opposite
transparent	glass	bottles	opaque
	Perspex	windows	
waterproof	plastics	umbrellas	absorbent
	metals	cars	
strong	steel	bridges	brittle
	concrete	buildings	
flexible	plastic	hosepipes	rigid
	leather	shoes	
hard	diamond	cutting tools	soft
	granite	floors	
magnetic	steel	magnets	non-magnetic
	iron		

See Q3

How are materials chosen?

Some objects are made from a range of materials. The choice of materials depends on the job they are needed to do.

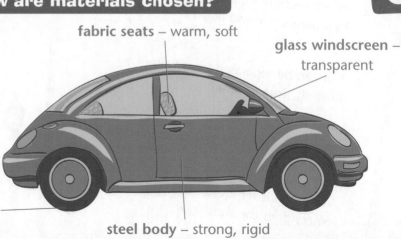

fabric seats – warm, soft

glass windscreen – transparent

rubber tyres – soft, good grip

steel body – strong, rigid

Q1

Circle the natural materials in the list below.

oil   silver   nylon

silk   fibre glass

Q2

Find these material properties and their opposites in the grid.

t	s	r	e	w	q	u	o	t	p	e
f	t	f	d	k	s	i	h	n	l	l
t	r	a	n	s	p	a	r	e	n	t
w	o	b	f	g	q	e	h	b	x	t
e	n	m	g	r	u	k	d	r	q	i
g	g	l	h	q	s	i	k	o	j	r
x	j	k	a	e	g	x	z	s	h	b
e	k	p	k	i	a	z	c	b	v	m
f	o	o	r	p	r	e	t	a	w	n
a	i	p	r	k	w	d	q	x	c	v
z	c	f	l	e	x	i	b	l	e	b

absorbent	waterproof
brittle	strong
flexible	rigid
transparent	opaque

Q3

Choose the materials and properties to complete the labels on the house.

Materials:
concrete
glass
plastic

Properties:
waterproof
strong
transparent

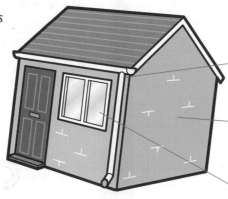

drainpipe made from ....

because it is ....

wall made from ....

because it is ....

window made from ....

because it is ....

Quick Quiz

1 What is a natural material?

....

2 Name a material that is attracted to magnets.

....

3 Name a flexible material.

....

4 Why would cotton not be a good material for an umbrella?

....

5 Why is steel used to make car bodies?

Did You Know?

Diamond is the hardest natural material.

Conductors and insulators

What is a thermal conductor?

See Q1

A **thermal conductor** lets heat travel through it **easily**. Most **metals** are good thermal conductors, e.g. aluminium, copper and steel. A cooking pan is made of metal so the heat from the cooker ring can quickly pass through the pan to the food inside it.

See Q2

What is a thermal insulator?

A **thermal insulator** makes it **difficult** for heat to travel through it. Thermal insulators include **wood**, **plastic**, **wool** and **polystyrene**. A wooden spoon is used to stir hot liquids in a pan, to stop the heat from travelling to your hand.

What is an electrical conductor?

See Q3

An **electrical conductor** lets electricity flow through it **easily**. **Metals** are generally good conductors of electricity. This is why all electrical items have metal parts and wires.

See Q4

What is an electrical insulator?

An **electrical insulator** makes it **difficult** for electricity to flow through it. Most non-metals are good electrical insulators, e.g. **plastic**, **glass** and **rubber**. For safety, these materials are used in electrical items to prevent us from touching the metal parts that conduct the electricity.

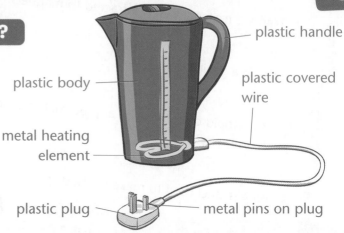

plastic handle

plastic body

plastic covered wire

metal heating element

plastic plug

metal pins on plug

Q1

Circle the materials that are good thermal conductors.

steel   wood

plastic   iron

Q2

a) What is a thermal insulator?

....

....

b) Why do you think that many cooking pans have plastic or wood handles?

....

....

....

Q3

Which of these is **not** an electrical conductor? Circle your answer.

copper   steel

gold   paper

Q4

Tick the correct statement to complete this sentence.

The wire has a plastic coating because...

a) it is a good thermal insulator. ☐

b) it is a good electrical conductor. ☐

c) it is a good electrical insulator. ☐

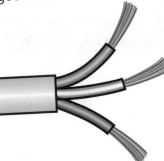

Quick Quiz

1 Name a material that is a good electrical conductor.

....

2 Why is it a good idea for an electrician to wear rubber gloves?

....

3 Aluminium is a good thermal conductor. True or false?

....

4 Name a material that is both a good thermal and electrical insulator.

....

5 Why are some winter clothes made from wool?

....

Did You Know?

Tall buildings often have a thick copper strip on top of them to act as a lightning conductor. It conducts the electricity from the lightning safely down to the ground.

Rocks and soils

See Q1

What type of materials are rocks?

Rocks are **natural** materials. Some rocks are **harder** than others, such as granite and marble. Some rocks, such as sandstone and chalk, are **soft**.

See Q2

Are rocks waterproof?

Some rocks do not let water soak through them. They are **impermeable** (waterproof). Marble and slate are impermeable, this is why they are used for roofs and floors. Some rocks, such as sandstone and limestone, let water soak through them. They are **permeable**.

See Q3

What is soil made from?

Soil is made up of tiny bits of rock, dead plants and animals, air and water. There are different types of soils.

See Q4

What are the different types of soils?

	Type of soil	Texture	Air gaps	Water drainage
	sandy	dry	lots of small gaps	good
	gravelly	small stones and pebbles	bigger gaps	very good
	clay	heavy and sticky	not many gaps	bad

Q1

a) Name a hard rock.

....

b) Name a soft rock.

....

Q2

Complete these sentences by filling in the blanks.

a) Rocks that let water soak through them are called ....

b) Rocks that do not let water through them are called ....

Q3

Which of these is **not** present in soil? Circle the odd one out.

dead plants   air

water   glass

Q4

Draw lines to match each type of soil to its description.

clay soil   very good drainage

gravelly soil   big air gaps

sandy soil   heavy and sticky

Quick Quiz

1   What type of materials are rocks?

....

2   Why is slate used to make roof tiles?

....

3   Name two things that can be found in soil.

....

4   Which type of soil has very few air gaps?

....

5   Which type of soil contains lots of stones and pebbles?

....

Did You Know?

Alum Bay is a sandy bay on the Isle of Wight. The bay is famous for its multi-coloured sands.

Scientific investigation

How should I carry out an investigation?

An investigation must have a **purpose**. You need to **plan** the investigation, work out what you will **measure** and what **equipment** you need. You need to decide how you will record and display the **results**. Finally, you need to work out a **conclusion**.

See Q1

What is a fair test?

See Q2

A **fair test** is when you use the same equipment for each test, measure things accurately and make sure that you carry out each test in exactly the same way.

Is safety important?

See Q3

It is important to carry out tests safely. In some tests you may need to use burners, candles, scissors, glass containers or hot liquids. You should wear protective clothing, work sensibly and wash your hands when you have finished.

How should I present my results?

See Q4

Results should be recorded in a logical way. You can use **tables**, **charts** and **graphs**.

This line graph shows that the longer a candle burns, the less it weighs.

Q1

Put these steps into the correct order.

a) Work out a conclusion.

b) Choose your equipment.

c) Decide on the purpose.

d) Record your results.

☐ ☐ ☐ ☐

Q2

Tick the two correct answers to complete this sentence. To carry out a fair test it is important to...

a) use the same equipment for each test. ☐

b) measure things accurately. ☐

c) change the conditions of the test. ☐

d) wear gloves and goggles. ☐

Q3

Make a list of three things you should do to make sure you carry out an investigation safely.

1 ....

....

2 ....

....

3 ....

....

Q4

Tick which method you **wouldn't** use to present your results.

table ☐   graph ☐

conclusion ☐   chart ☐

Quick Quiz

1 What must an investigation have?

....

2 What is the last step in an investigation?

....

3 Each test in an investigation should be carried out differently. True or false?

....

4 Give two possible dangers you could meet in an investigation.

....

5 Give a way in which your results for an investigation could be recorded.

....

Answers

Earth, moon and sun (page 3)

Q1 **b)** No the sun doesn't move

Q2 **a)** To travel around, or the path of a planet or moon
   b) Gravity
   c) 365 days

Q3 **b)** The rotation of the earth on its axis

Q4 The order should read from top to bottom: 2, 1, 4, 5, 3

Quick Quiz

1 24 hours
2 It is day (light)
3 It is a sphere
4 28 days
5 It is a sphere

Sound (page 5)

Q1 **a)** Vibrate   **b)** TV, voice, bell or similar

Q2 Water, metal, glass

Q3 From left to right: blow hard; hit gently; pluck gently; pluck hard

Q4 **a)** Higher   **b)** low

Quick Quiz

1 Pitch
2 Yes
3 A space with no air in it
4 Silence
5 Loudness

Light and shadow (page 7)

Q1 Mirror

Q2 Tissue paper – translucent; bottle – transparent; cardboard – opaque

Q3 CD, mirror, foil

Q4 Shadow

Q5 False

Quick Quiz

1 In straight lines
2 Shiny objects
3 Will not let light pass through
4 Translucent
5 Sun

Electricity (page 9)

Q1 Mains, battery, mains, battery

Q2 **c)**

Q3 To break the flow of electricity in a circuit

Q4 **b)**

Quick Quiz

1 The bulb will shine more brightly

2

3 Switch
4 Battery or cell
5 Any from: batteries may be flat, bulb may be broken or wires may not be connected correctly.

Forces (page 11)

Q1 **a)** A push or a pull   **b)** newtons

Q2 Picture **b)**

Q3 **c)**

Q4 Weight

Quick Quiz

1 Forcemeter
2 Use arrows
3 Unbalanced
4 Balanced
5 The force of gravity pulls the pencil towards the earth.

Types of forces (page 13)

Q1 Float

Q2 Car tyres – want friction; ice skates – don't want friction; trainers – want friction

Q3 Draw a smaller arrow pointing upwards

Q4 Repel, repel, attract

Quick Quiz

1 Rough
2 Poles
3 Air resistance
4 The object sinks
5 They attract each other

Living things (page 15)

Q1 Breathe, reproduce, grow

Q2 **a)** Seed, seedling, plant   **b)** embryo, baby, adult

Q3 Nutrition

Q4 Reproduction, seeds

Q5 **a)** True   **b)** true   **c)** false

Quick Quiz

1 Any 2 from: grow, breathe, feed, reproduce, have sensitivity, movement, ability to get rid of waste
2 Growth
3 Leaves
4 Seeds
5 Turn towards light

Classification and keys (page 17)

Q1 By their characteristics (things they have in common)

Q2 **b)** Flowering and non-flowering plants

Q3 Vertebrates – parrot, frog, dog; invertebrates – worm, slug, woodlouse

Q4 Ant

Quick Quiz

1 An animal with a backbone
2 Beetle, slug, worm or similar
3 To identify an unknown living thing
4 True
5 Amphibians

Habitats and adaptation (page 19)

Q1 A place where a plant or animal lives

Q2 Frog – pond; earthworm – soil; fern – shade; thrush – hedges and trees

Q3 **a)** It breathes through gills   **e)** it has fins

Quick Quiz

1 Desert
2 In a pond
3 To catch fish
4 Sharp beak or has talons that grip
5 Penguin, polar bear, arctic fox or similar

Food chains (page 21)

Q1 Lettuce → slug → hedgehog
Q2 Producers – lettuce, grass; consumers – greenfly, slug, rabbit
Q3 **a)** An animal that preys on other animals.
    b) The animal that is eaten by another animal.
Q4 Rabbit

Quick Quiz

1 Green plant
2 Producers
3 Consumers
4 Yes
5 True

Plant growth (page 23)

Q1 Stem – carries water; leaf – makes food; roots – anchor the plant; flower – used in reproduction

Q2 Starting from top, reading clockwise: seed, young plant, adult plant, plant dies
Q3 Nutrients, light, heat, water
Q4 **a)** Lack of light

Quick Quiz

1 Roots
2 Dry and shrivelled
3 To make food
4 Germination
5 Any 2 from: heat, light, water, nutrients, air

Flowering plants (page 25)

Q1 Stamen – male part of flower; ovary – where seeds are stored; petal – attracts insects

Q2 1. By insects 2. by the wind
Q3 **c)** Carried by a bee

Quick Quiz

1 Stigma, style, ovary
2 So insects can carry it to other flowers
3 Blown by the wind
4 Seeds
5 By animals eating them and passing them in their droppings.

Human body (page 27)

Q1 **a)** Plaque **b)** canine
Q2 Plaque, twice, floss, tooth
Q3 Your route should go through: a skeleton is jointed → the skeleton enables movement → ligaments hold joints together → ribs protect heart and lungs

Quick Quiz

1 Pull
2 Molar
3 Yes muscles work in pairs
4 Calcium
5 Meat

Health and healthy eating (page 29)

Q1 Fish and meat – protein; grapes – vitamins and minerals; butter – fats; cornflakes – carbohydrates

Q2 Blood, heart, oxygen, carbon dioxide
Q3 **a)** Heart rate **b)** it increases heart rate and makes the heart stronger
Q4 Too much alcohol and smoking

Quick Quiz

1 Fats and carbohydrates
2 Good digestion
3 Heart
4 It will increase
5 Oxygen

Micro-organisms (page 31)

Q1 Microscope
Q2 Mould, bacteria, virus
Q3 Any three from: wash hands before eating and after going to toilet, cover nose and mouth when sneezing, keep away from people with infections, do not eat food which is not fresh or properly cooked.
Q4 Yeast

Quick Quiz

1 A small living thing
2 Any 2 from: in food, water, air, inside humans and animals
3 Bacteria
4 Virus
5 To prevent the spread of harmful bacteria

States of matter (page 33)

Q1 **a)** Definite **b)** be held
Q2 Water, syrup, milk
Q3 **a)** It does not flow **d)** it is usually invisible
Q4 **a)** Liquid, gas **b)** liquid, solid

Quick Quiz

1 Solid
2 Gas
3 Solid
4 Liquid
5 Gas

Reversible and non-reversible changes (page 35)

Q1 **a)** Reversible **b)** freezes, melts
Q2 d, b, a, c
Q3 **a)** Non-reversible **b)** you cannot get back the egg in its original state

Quick Quiz

1 Reversible
2 False
3 Reversible
4 Physical
5 Gas or vapour

Mixing materials (page 37)

Q1 A solution
Q2 Both sugar and flour; just the sand; neither
Q3 Filtering
Q4 Heat the mixture to evaporate the water from the salt
Q5 **c)** Vinegar and bicarbonate of soda

Quick Quiz

1 Two or more materials
2 Sieve
3 False
4 No
5 It evaporates

Properties of materials (page 39)

Q1 Oil, silver, silk

Q2

t	s	r	e	w	q	u	o	t	p	e
f	t	f	d	k	s	i	h	n	l	l
t	r	a	n	s	p	a	r	e	n	t
w	o	b	f	g	q	e	h	b	x	t
e	n	m	g	r	u	k	d	r	q	i
g	g	l	h	q	s	i	k	o	j	r
x	j	k	a	e	g	x	z	s	h	b
e	k	p	k	i	a	z	c	b	v	m
f	o	o	r	p	r	e	t	a	w	n
a	i	p	r	k	w	d	q	x	c	v
z	c	f	l	e	x	i	b	l	e	b

Q3 Drainpipe – plastic, waterproof; wall – concrete, strong; window – glass, transparent

1   A material found in nature
2   Steel or iron
3   Rubber
4   It is absorbent so would soak up water
5   It is strong and rigid

Conductors and insulators (page 41)

Q1 Steel, iron
Q2 a) A material that does not let heat pass through it easily.
b) They are good thermal insulators so do not let heat travel through them easily.
Q3 Paper
Q4 c) It is a good electrical insulator

1   Any metal
2   Rubber is a good electrical insulator
3   True
4   Plastic
5   Wool is a good thermal insulator

Rocks and soils (page 43)

1   a) Granite or marble   b) sandstone or chalk
2   a) Permeable   b) impermeable
3   Glass
4   Clay soil – heavy and sticky; gravelly soil – big air gaps; sandy soil – very good drainage

1   Natural
2   It is impermeable (waterproof)
3   Any 2 from: dead plants and animals, air, water, tiny bits of rock
4   Clay soil
5   Gravelly soil

Scientific investigation (page 45)

Q1 c, b, d, a
Q2 a) Use the same equipment for each test   b) measure things accurately
Q3 Wear protective clothing, work sensibly, wash your hands
Q4 Conclusion

1   A purpose
2   Working out a conclusion
3   False
4   Any 2 from: hot liquids, flames or glass equipment
5   In a table, chart or graph